GAS TURBINE ANALYSIS AND PRACTICE

GAS TURBINE ANALYSIS AND PRACTICE

BURGESS H. JENNINGS

Professor and Chairman
Department of Mechanical Engineering
The Technological Institute, Northwestern University

WILLARD L. ROGERS

Assistant Professor of Mechanical Engineering
The Technological Institute, Northwestern University

New York   Toronto   London
McGRAW-HILL BOOK COMPANY, INC.
1953

GAS TURBINE ANALYSIS AND PRACTICE

THE MAPLE PRESS COMPANY, YORK, PA.

PREFACE

This text on gas turbines was prepared by the authors to meet the need for a book presenting a broad, but not detailed, coverage of the operating characteristics, industrial scope, and position that the gas turbine now holds and will attain in coming years. When the authors started writing the manuscript some years ago, suitable text material was practically nonexistent. Since that time, several books have appeared on the market. However, the authors hope that this text will simplify the teaching of this important subject and believe some of the methods of presentation to be sufficiently different to merit an additional book in the field.

It is assumed that the readers have some knowledge of basic thermodynamics and mechanics. The material presented in this text deals specifically with the types of problems associated with gas compression and gas-turbine operations. For these applications the required basic considerations are given in some detail. The authors have prepared a set of tables of air properties, which are included for convenience in the text to simplify the work required in solving problems.

Up to the present time, by far the greatest use of the gas turbine has been in the field of aircraft propulsion, where it is supplanting in many instances the reciprocating engine. For this reason, it was felt desirable to give some coverage of the characteristics of the reciprocating internal-combustion engine as well as the gas turbine so that each type of unit could be placed in its proper perspective as a propulsion drive. The broad picture of the gas turbine as a prime mover in its own right has been adequately covered for potential uses in railway transportation and marine applications and for general power purposes.

Thermodynamic and flow-theory approaches to fundamental design and layout objectives are used. Although aerodynamic aspects of blading in compressors and turbines are discussed, they are not emphasized. The literature has been freely consulted, and a comprehensive bibliography of reference material is included in each chapter.

The authors appreciate the fine cooperation they received from a host of manufacturers, who furnished data, illustrative material, and basic information in regard to production and planned units. Credit lines for references and material used appear throughout the book.

This text is designed for a semester course meeting three times a week or for a briefer coverage in a similar class meeting for a quarter.

It is hoped that this book, in addition to meeting the need for a brief but comprehensive text, can furnish practicing engineers with reference data and an adequate background to enable them to understand the gas-turbine field.

B. H. JENNINGS
W. L. ROGERS

EVANSTON, ILL.
JANUARY, 1953

CONTENTS

CHAPTER 1

DEVELOPMENT OF THE INTERNAL-COMBUSTION ENGINE AND TURBINE

1-1. General Historical Background. From the latter part of the eighteenth century and continuing into the twentieth century, the industrial world thrived and prospered in what might be called an *age of steam*. During this time the steam engine grew to full stature, reaching a peak with the enormous central-station engines which were in widespread use during the early part of this century. However, the importance of steam engines declined as steam turbines, which were first introduced about 1880, developed into the efficient and versatile units of the present day. The last stronghold of the steam engine was the railway locomotive, but more and more of these familiar "iron horses" are being converted into scrap iron, and their days are apparently numbered.

During the latter half of the nineteenth century, an additional competitor to the steam engine began to appear in various types of reciprocating internal-combustion engines. These early engines employed a combustible mixture of air and gaseous (or volatile-liquid) fuel which was ignited either by direct flame or by some sort of spark ignition. A still later development in this field (1892) was the diesel engine, which did not need a spark for ignition. In the diesel engine, fuel was sprayed into a chamber of air which, as a result of rapid compression, had reached a sufficiently high temperature to cause spontaneous ignition of the fuel.

In the present century the spark-ignition engine has reached a high degree of perfection in current automotive and airplane engines. The diesel engine has likewise been greatly improved and in one field, that of railroad propulsion, has reached a position of outstanding leadership.

Just as the steam turbine followed the reciprocating steam engine at a later date, a similar pattern held for the gas turbine. The gas turbine, as a satisfactory commercial device, did not appear until the internal-combustion engine had reached a very advanced stage of development and usage. The gas turbine and its air compressor are high-rotative-speed machines, and the passages for compressing and expanding the air must follow aerodynamic design principles and meet requirements for high thermodynamic effectiveness as well. The design experience of steam-turbine practice was available to gas-turbine builders. However,

1

steam-turbine designers had not considered the reversed problem of compression, nor had operating practice with steam extended much above 1000 F, whereas gas-turbine temperatures of 1200 to 1500 F were needed. High gas-turbine temperatures required metals capable of operating at elevated temperatures under stressed conditions. Both design features and metallurgical developments have progressed to where the gas turbine is becoming an increasingly significant prime mover in many fields of power.

The first extensive use of gas turbines was in connection with the supercharging of reciprocating internal-combustion engines. The gas turbine is also a type of internal-combustion engine, and to place the turbine in its proper perspective, a brief background of the reciprocating engine will be presented before formally developing the turbine.

1-2. The Reciprocating Engine. What might be called the fore-runners of modern reciprocating gasoline engines were the gas engines developed to working form by Lenoir, Otto, and Langen in the period between 1860 and 1880. A Frenchman, Beau de Rochas, in 1864 proposed a cycle which closely resembles the modern cycle. In his proposal, he explained the advantages of compression before ignition and effective use of a large ratio of expansion. Otto, using the ideas of de Rochas, developed a four-stroke cycle which was so outstanding and successful that the name of de Rochas almost lapsed into obscurity and the general four-stroke pattern and its prototype cycle came to be associated with the name of Otto.

From these early engine attempts, the reciprocating gasoline engine has been developed to reach the high degree of perfection which it holds in present-day automotive and aircraft engines. Most modern engines use gasoline as fuel with high-tension spark ignition. They range from single-cylinder to multicylinder units which in some cases have employed 28 cylinders. Automotive units are usually of *in-line* or *V-type* designs, using liquid cooling for the six or eight cylinders which usually constitute the engine. Aircraft engines are most frequently of the radial air-cooled type, although liquid-cooled V-type units have also been employed.

Most spark-ignition engines operate on the four-stroke principle, which is shown diagrammatically in Fig. 1-1. The suction stroke first occurs with the inlet valve open and the piston drawing in a combustible charge of fuel and air. On the second stroke, with both valves closed, the piston compresses the charge. Near the end of the compression stroke, ignition is started from the electric-spark device (appearing between the valves in the figure), and the rapid rise in temperature and pressure of the gases accelerates the piston downward on its power stroke with the valves continuing in the closed position. Near the end of this stroke, the exhaust valve opens, and on the following return stroke the

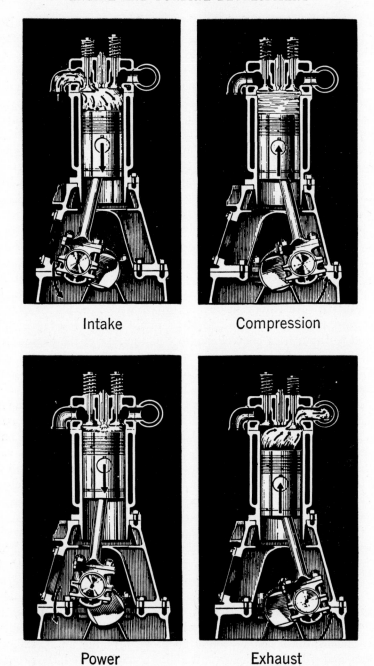

FIG. 1-1.   Four-stroke-cycle events shown in connection with a stationary-type engine.

exhaust gases are expelled from the cylinder. Thus the cylinder is ready to receive a fresh charge on the next downstroke. It can be shown how the economy of such an engine is influenced by the *ratio of compression* of the gases (*viz.*, the volume occupied by the gases at the start of compression compared with the volume occupied after compression). In an engine of this type, the combustible mixture may consist of gaseous fuel and air or of liquid fuel delivered by a carburetor into the air stream entering the engine in such quantity that after atomization and subsequent vaporization a combustible mixture exists in the engine cylinder.

1-3. Reciprocating Aircraft Engines. In reciprocating spark-ignition engines a zenith was probably reached in the multirow radial aircraft engine. The engine shares with the gas turbine an important position in the field of aircraft propulsion. In particular for commercial and large transport airplanes at moderate speeds, the reciprocating engine is still the predominant drive. A recent development has been a combination of such an engine with integrated gas turbines for utilizing a portion of the energy in the exhaust gases which otherwise would largely be wasted.

Figure 1-2 is a three-quarter front view of a Wright Cyclone engine, model C18BD. Air enters the engine through a scoop so placed as to use the forward motion of the airplane to produce ram effect. This air is ducted to the master control chamber at the rear of the engine, from which it passes to the supercharger, where it is compressed to a pressure above the atmospheric pressure existing at the flight altitude of the plane. This compressed air then flows through tubing to each of the 18 cylinders. With the intake valve of a particular cylinder open, the piston moves toward the center of the engine, drawing in air while the fuel pump injects gasoline directly into the cylinder. The piston then returns on its compression stroke, and, with both the intake and the exhaust valve closed, the mixture is compressed into the combustion chamber at the top of the cylinder. Near the end of this compression stroke, the charge is ignited by dual spark plugs, and the power stroke then takes place with the intake and exhaust valves remaining closed. On the next stroke, the exhaust valve opens, and the burned gases are pushed into the exhaust pipe.

Observation of Fig. 1-2 will show that the engine has two parallel rows of cylinders. Each of these rows consists of nine cylinders with the firing so arranged that every other cylinder in a row fires in sequence, *viz.*, 1-3-5-7-9-2-4-6-8-1. The nose part of the engine contains planetary reduction gearing which reduces the speed of the propeller hub to less than half engine speed. This is necessary because propeller-tip speeds should be kept below the speed of sound to prevent undue noise, excessive vibration, and reduced efficiency. With lower engine speed, the propeller blades can be made longer, and if, in addition, they are given a deep pitch, a large amount of engine power is utilized per revolution of the propeller.

This particular engine has a cylinder bore of 6.125 in. and a stroke of 6.312 in. which, for the 18 cylinders, gives a piston displacement of 3347 in.[3] The volume compression ratio is 6.5:1. This engine is provided with a centrifugal-type supercharger of which the 13-in.-diameter impeller is driven either at 6.46 or 8.67 times crankshaft speed. The supercharger compresses the air supplied to the engine. The engine develops 2500 hp at 2800 rpm during take-off, with cruising horsepower 1470 at 2300 rpm. The engine weighs 2884 lb without starter and has an over-all diameter of 55.6 in. and length of 78.5 in.

Fig. 1-2. Eighteen-cylinder reciprocating aircraft engine, Wright Cyclone C18BD. (*Wright Aeronautical Corp.*)

1-4. Diesel Engines. Early internal-combustion engines required either a spark or a flame to ignite the mixture charged into the cylinder. This charge consisted either of a combustible mixture of gas and air or of a volatile-liquid fuel with the air. Toward the end of the nineteenth century, increasing interest appeared in an engine which would compress air and then burn fuel injected into compressed air. One of the first successful engines of this type was the Hornsby-Ackroyd engine. This was a conventionally built engine except for an uncooled bulbous portion built into the cylinder head. Into this bulb, liquid fuel could be sprayed at timed intervals and ignited by the hot metal. The Hornsby-Ackroyd engine was the forerunner of a group of so-called "hot-bulb," "hot-spot," or "semidiesel" engines.

Several years after the development of hot-spot engines, Rudolph Diesel in 1892 obtained a patent on an engine which could compress the air by such an amount that the resulting temperature rise of the air would be sufficiently high to ignite any fuel which might be injected into the air. Diesel's first engine envisaged the use of pulverized coal injected into the compressed air, but this idea was never successful, and the greater part of Diesel's development was concerned with the use of a fuel oil sprayed into the hot compressed air.   Progress on the diesel engine was not very rapid until after the original Diesel patents expired in 1913.   However, before that time this type of engine had clearly demonstrated itself as an efficient and effective prime mover.

To inject the fuel oil into the cylinder of the engine, the early diesel engines used a separate high-pressure air compressor operating at a pressure higher than that which existed in the engine cylinder.   Later and present-day engines have largely given up this so-called "air" injection and use suitable mechanically operated force-feed pumps which inject finely atomized fuel oil at high pressures into the engine cylinder or into a precombustion chamber.

Figure 1-1 shows the essential arrangement of a four-stroke-cycle engine.   The same outline applies either to a diesel engine or to a spark-ignition engine.   For the diesel engine, no spark is required, and a fuel-injection or spray valve appears instead of a spark device near the center of the cylinder head.   In the diesel engine, the charge of air in the cylinder must be compressed through a much greater range than in the spark-ignition engine.   In spark-ignition engines, volume-compression ratios from 6:1 to 8:1 are employed, whereas the diesel engine, in order to attain high temperatures from compression alone, requires ratios ranging from 14:1 up to 20:1.   For example, if ordinary air is compressed through a volume ratio of 16:1, the resulting temperature of the air rises to about 1100 F.   This air is sufficiently hot so that when atomized fuel oil is injected into it combustion starts and no additional form of ignition is required.   Compression ratio is defined as the volume occupied by the gas at the beginning of the compression stroke divided by the volume occupied by this gas at the end of the compression stroke.

Many engines work on the four-stroke cycle as previously described, but a two-stroke cycle, particularly in diesel engines, has also been found to be effective.   As the two-stroke cycle uses only two passages of the piston to complete a working cycle, it can sometimes result in a lighter weight unit for a given horsepower output.   In such an engine, exhaust and charging take place while the piston is moving near the bottom of its stroke and the crank is turning through 60° or less.   Most engines of this type employ a separate scavenging air compressor which not only can supply the air required but can give it a slight supercharge as well,